D1593021

There's an Otter in my Water

Poems for the family

Written by ————
Edwin Padlan
and Micah Padlan

Illustrated by
Neda Sadreddin

There's an Otter in my Water
Poems for the family
Copyright © 2020 by Edwin Padlan
Illustrated by Neda Sadreddin

Published by Alma Holdings
Edited by Jean Meyer
First Edition
10 9 8 7 6 5 4 3 2 1

ISBN 978-1-7357544-1-3

For Micah, my inspiration.

GROWING UP

The biggest number in the whole wide world
Is more than I can count -
Like all the things I can become,
An infinite amount.

ADVENTURE

Singapore, I quite adore.
Prague's a classic city.
New York nights are drowned in lights.
Fontainebleau's so pretty.

Philly is a hidden gem.
Sydney water's swell.
Montreal is summer love.
Christchurch rings a bell.

Hong Kong's pace is speedy.
Tokyo food's a dream.
Istanbul's so beautiful.
Cape Town's wines - supreme.

Botswana's animals are wild.
Dubai is so creative.
Iguazu Falls - spectacular.
San Fran is innovative.

Let's go on a journey!
Stop to look and see.
Yes, home is where the heart is,
But adventure sets us free.

FAVORITE COLOR

Avocado, frogs and pickles,
Lime, wasabi, peas,
Alligator, seaweed, grass,
Berets and worn fatigues,

Turtle, beans,
Kale, seaweed,
Kiwi, moss, and envy,
Wreaths and leaves,
Apples, ferns,
Vines and poison ivy,

Grapes and emeralds galore,
Dinosaurs and jade,
Lettuce, scallions, forest, cacti,
Money, mint, and grassy glade,

Olive, bugs,
trees and slime,
And all things in between.

Bet you didn't realize that my favorite color's ...

ME DAY

I think about all of the years that have gone,
The battles I've lost,
And the victories I've won.

Today is the day I am totally free,
To focus on now,
And to celebrate me.

COWS RUN TOO

I ran to the store to get some milk,
But the grocer said "no moo."

"And we don't have meat nor similar ilk
Since those clever cows ran too."

Toodaloo!

QUESTION MACHINE

Go ahead and ask your question.
It'll only cost a penny.
Just drop the coins in the giant bin
and I'll answer one, or many.

Five more queries? Then write them down
And put the paper in the slot.
A nickel more - whatcha waiting for?
Do you want to learn, or not?

A dime for ten insights from my guiding light.
All the answers that you seek.
Speak with might and tone in the microphone,
To keep your winning streak.

More questions you say? Keep sending my way.
All day and all night, there's no end.
Only twenty five cents. There's no need to be tense.
Be relaxed. Ask your question, my friend.

A hundred answers to a hundred questions
Is that all that you desire?
Insert a dollar, prepare to learn,
And set your mind on fire.

The money you gave is worth infinite less
Than the knowledge you have earned.
So the coins and bills that you gave to me
Will entirely be returned.

All I ask of you is to pay it forward.
On another child, leave an impression.
Help a curious kin. Be an answer machine
When someone else has a question.

CHUNK-O-SALMON

What should I do with a chunk-o-salmon?

Chop it
Or slop it?
Mop it
When I drop it?

Bake it or
Make it a
Creamy
Milkshake it?

Splay it or
Tray it?
Plate it or
Grate it?

Lookit!
Don't cook it.
Raw fish is
Off the hook it.

Don't be late, it
Won't be great, it's
Too good to wait, it's ...

Gulp.

Delish.
I ate it.

HUMMINGCOPTER

Hummingbirds, they fly with grace.
Flapping their wings like figure eights.
Up, down, left, right,
Forward and back at a blistering pace.

Like helicopters - they fly in place,
Very uniquely in time and space.

You don't believe me?
Well, look at my face.
My eyes full of wonder
While they enter my space
Of lavender trees, with a warm embrace.

Enjoy the moment.

They'll flee with no trace.
Natural wonders you cannot replace.

SOAR

The girl from tiny village -
She sprouted wings and didn't know
That as she labored hard, so hard -
A secret power - she would grow.

Safely on the stable ground,
She lifted friends so high.
Fixed on what's in front of her,
She never knew that she could fly.

She sailed across the treacherous sea
In search of sunken treasure.
She battled wind and waves so high,
But nothing could capsize her.

She unearthed ancient ruins -
Her hands and arms exhausted.
She scaled the mountains oh so high,
Her feet got cold and frosted.

She couldn't climb much higher now
Despite how much she tried.
Cast down, she never realized
Her power, locked inside.

She worried that her strength was gone -
Would perish in a year,
And didn't know her mighty wings
Could cross the atmosphere.

And now atop the grandest peak
She doubted what's in store.
Someday she'll grow to realize
That now it's time to soar.

SLAP-A-DOODLE

Have you seen my slap-a-doodle?
It's one part silly and another part noodle.

It's a smidge of happy
And a dash of string.
Has a drop of color
And a pinch of bling.

I roll it and twist it to dream and play.
I flick it and fling it to my delight all day.

When it flops around, do you thinks it's roodle?
Have you seen my slap-a-doodle?

FRIEND SHIP

Come take a ride on my friend ship.
Adventure awaits.
Let's go. Set sail!

Just give to me
A gentle breeze
And I'll respond with a gale.

BIRDNOKEYNOSE

Fish cheese. Swiss cheese.
High in the sky moon cheese.

Potato wing. Elephant wing.
Flying things are like birds when they sing.

Mouse on the house eats the cheese.
The house with wings - fly me to the moon, please.

Birds can't fly since I stole all their wings.
Nope that's a lie,
I wouldn't do such a thing.

CREATE

Blue banana
Pink raccoon
Striped potato
Spotted loon

Painted night
And speedy snails
Life-sized chess
And tiny whales

Shiny streets
And sugary dills
Checkered floors
And flattened hills

New inventions
Healing cure
Sushi pizza
Gross, I'm sure.

New ideas will stimulate.

There is no wrong when you create.

THERE'S AN OTTER IN MY WATER

"There's an otter in my water," said a man to the maitre d.'
It was barking a song while it swam along
Like it's frolicking 'round in the sea.

"There's a sloth in my broth," said a girl to her dad.
She acted most prim, "'Tis no place to swim.
Silly sloth, you're making me mad."

"There's a gnu in my stew," said a teen to her friend.
She asked it to halt in mid somersault
And the gnu judges scored it a ten.

"There's a goose in my juice," said a man to the ladies.
It was honking a tune with a loon and baboon,
Who then harmonized songs from the eighties.

"There's a clam in my chowder" said a boy to his mama.
"Son, that's something I'd want in this fine restaurant!"
"But mom, it's wearing a pink striped pajama!"

THE BEST

Yoga on Monday.
Running on Tuesday.
Weights on Wednesday.
Tennis on Thursday.
Frisbee on Friday.
Swimming on Saturday.
Hard to decide which one is the best.
Yay, it's Sunday.
It's my day to rest.

THE OTHER SIDE

"The grass is greener,"
They always say.
I don't quite understand.

As the rest of the world
Seeks their other side,
I'm grateful for where I stand.

RAYS DOWN HERE

Mom, please roll the window down
So I can tell the sky,
"Hi, Sun and Clouds, the gloom and gray
All need to say goodbye.

The sky is full of shades of pale.
It can't get any duller.
Clouds, please sprinkle misty water
And grace us with some color.

Sun, please shine your light just right
So vibrant rainbows can appear.
You're always shining way up there,
Please send your rays down here."

THE FLOWERS ARE TALKING

If you pause for just a moment,
You'll hear the flowers talking.

Close your eyes and listen closely
And stop your thoughts from walking.

The wind will whoosh, the birds will sing,
The waves will crash, and the bees will sting.

But the flower's there, it's just a-wishin'
For you to stop ...and listen.

MOUNTAIN VIEW

I view mountains from my window.
I view mountains from the car.
I drive and drive a hundred miles
And see mountains near and far.

I fly to towering peaks and points
I view mountains in the sky.
I sail to distant islands
And see mountains oh so high.

I explore the pile, the crag, the cliff,
The ridge, the hill, and bluff.
The snowy grass, the rocky steep,
And bare undamaged rough.

I view mountains from the corners,
From the top, and from the side.
I claim victory, as I reach the peak,
And I discover diamonds deep inside.

Despite the journey far and wide
Atop the highest dome.
It comforts me when I view mountains -
I always feel at home.

JUMPING COW

I ate a jumping cow for lunch
And now I can't stand still.
I hop just like a rabbit
And bound around at will.

When I leap, I leap so high.
The birds give me a stare.
Can you see me way up here
From all the way down there?

I prance around, my feet on fire
As if I'm in a trance.
It's almost like the floor is lava
Or ants are in my pants.

I should watch out for things I eat.
Wish I could settle down.
I'll let this flying high wear off.
Land safely on the ground.

FIVE ROSES

One is a beauty.
One bud just born.
One is all bendy.
One has a thorn.
One is the mother of all the roses.
Each of their beauty's unique,
One supposes.

IN MY WORLD

I dig. I mine. I make a light.
I build. I fight. I sleep at night.
I craft a pick in just five clicks.
I make a sword with just one stick.
I run, I swim, I fly, I jump,
I walk straight through and do not bump.

I Make ten houses. Such tricky jobs.
I Invite my friends to defeat twelve mobs.
I Need a bed to sleep at night.
I Enchant my sword so I can fight.
I Create a world to invite my friend.
I Race through maps till I reach the end.
I Add some armor so I can defend.
I Fence some pigs to tame and tend.
I Type a message to you and send...

"Come join me. Have fun. It's cool. Let's play."
"Will you come explore in my world today?"

HAPPY LEMON

Good morn' my happy lemon!
What's it going to be today?
A little sour? A little spice?
Some smiles and sunshine will suffice.

A bit of bubbly
And something sweet.
A dash of lime
would make complete.

A lot of fire mixed with tang.
Two drops of tears or maybe five.
Hundreds more will show the reason
That you care and passion thrives.

Some peaks and valleys,
Bumps and hills,
Unhappy endings,
Sparks, and thrills.

But all in all,
please don't forget.
Whether sweet or sour,
Don't change one bit.

REPLAY

I stopped to smell the roses,
But got poked in the nose by a thorn.

I listened to my vinyls,
But found they were quite worn.

I meditated with my friend,
But felt no better in the morn.

I escaped all week to a private retreat,
But couldn't be reborn.

Then wrote some thoughts to clear my mind
And thanked the world for being kind,

Replayed great memories I could find,
And left my harmful thoughts behind.

ONE OUNCE

Every morning,
Mom drinks coffee,
More than just one ounce.

I know when it's time
For her energy boost.
No need
That she announce.

If she doesn't,
Like a tiger,
She will growl and she will pounce.

But afterwards,
I'm just not sure
If she'll be calm
Or will she bounce?

Smallish or enormous.
She likes any
And all amounts.

Doesn't matter.
She likes it all.
How many ounces?
Lost count.

FOUR-LEGGED DUCK

Have you ever seen a four-legged duck?
It chirps like a bird and honks like a truck.

It's limbs have red stripes, like a candy cane.
It's wings are so thin, like a paper airplane.

It purrs like a kitten when eating peach jelly
And stands like a meerkat to warm it's big belly.

It dances around if you give it a nickel.
It snorts and it cackles with barely a tickle.

It sleeps in a cave and hibernates daily.
It wakes in the night to play ukulele.

It wears orange boots when it guzzles iced tea
And a ten gallon hat made from bark of a tree.

You may never see it, but it's quite a dandy.
Just look for the duck eating pink cotton candy.

THE END OF THE RAINBOW

Where's the end of the rainbow?
Ask the leprechaun.

Is there a start or a finish?
Track it's path to the horizon.

Let me share with you a secret.
It's connected, all as one.

A circle, of refracted light.
No way! You're poking fun!

A fleeting gift of science.
See the colors in the dawn.

Look at that! It's so unique!

Oops.
Too late.
It's gone.

SLEEPOVER

Jump under the covers.
Turn on the flashlight.
Tell scary stories
And talk through the night.

Stay up 'til three
Then wake up at noon.
Eat chocolate pancakes
The whole afternoon.

Pillow fights. Pillow forts.
Play make believe.
Discover old toys
It's like Christmas eve.

Get embarrassed from 'Truth or Dare?'
Face turns all red.
Laugh ourselves silly,
Nearly wet the whole bed.

Stay in pajamas.
Video games.
TV and cookies
And laughing at memes.

Repeat it all over
Again the next day,
'Cuz summer vacation's
A three-month partay.

GROUND PLANE

I wish I had a ground plane.
It won't fly in the air.

A car with wings - so fast, so fast!
To take me anywhere.

Just tell the captain where to go
And don't forget to pay.

"Please take me to the Dana Street school.
The bell just rang. I'm late!"

PLAY WITH FIRE

You say,
"Kids shouldn't play with fire.
The hobby's just a phase."

I say,
"You should fuel the spark
And set their souls ablaze."

SUPERSONIC

With a supersonic boom,
He raced into the room.
He zigged and zagged,
And wigged and wagged,
From dawn until the noon.

Then all throughout the day,
We jumped, we laughed, we played.
We danced about.
He tired me out.
A break for him? No way!

With speed and style and might -
His energy full flight.
He clung to me,
Infinity,
Til time to say good night.

MADITUDE

My attitude has a long way to go.
It sank to a latitude so low.
But with gratitude in words written down,
My maditude turned upside down.

DANCE PARTY

Everyone should dance.
Please don't miss your chance.
If the dance floor's hot.
If the dance floor's not.
Everyone should dance.

Everyone should dance.
It puts you in a trance.
If you've two left feet or can't hear the beat,
If your tempo's wrong, just glide along.
Everyone should dance.

Everyone should dance.
It's like a sweet romance.
Any tune you find, keep it in your mind.
Fling your arms around, move them up and down.
Then you tap your boots to the root toot toots.
Spin around with a toss if you just can't floss.
Move your hips with flare.
Close your eyes,
Don't care.

Everyone should dance.

SUSHI FOR BREAKFAST

Sushi for breakfast
Sushi for lunch
Sushi for dinner
Sushi for brunch
Sushi for snack any time of the day
Sushi at midnight on a TV tray

Fake sushi keychain
And two sushi socks.
Six sushi puzzles
and a round sushi clock.

Salmon, hamachi and tuna tataki.
Ikura, eel, but no teriyaki.

Can't eat any more. That was my last maki.
I'm thirsty now. Can you please pass the sak--
    ...umm... lemonade.

COLLECTING ROCKS

Brown rock
White rock
Covered in moss green rock
White chalk
River rock
Slimy, grimy sea rock
Melt into glass sand rock
Hard as a diamond gem rock
Glowing and flowing lava rock
Dark as obsidian black rock
Festival of rock Woodstock
Four-leaf lucky shamrock
Giant formations stone block
Hide in my pockets pebble stock
Knapsack
Art smock
Filled to the top old sock
When tired of collecting these earth rocks,
I'll go high in the sky like an astronaut.
There is no holding me back talk.
I'll be the first to the red rock.

GIVE

Treat with care and respect,
Your body and mind,
And know that you simply are
One of a kind.

Stay true to yourself.
Get going.
Start livin'.

Be sure that you share
All the gifts you've been given.

BISHTILE

My pet is a Bishtile.
Its name is East.

It has super long wings
For protecting its feast,

A horn like a narwhal
For stirring concoctions,

And scales like a reptile
For weighing all options.

You don't think it's real?
Of a pair, it's just half.

It's sitting right next to
My cheerful bear-affe.

DAD'S SHIRTS

One shirt's from Pamplona.
The other's from Big Red.
The sesame shirt's in my hand.
His yellow shirt's on my head.

The mousy shirt fell on the floor.
The light brown, on the chair.
His 'peace sign' shirt is faded blue.
How is the green one over there?

"Son,...

One day my shirts will all be worn
With holes and tattered sleeve.

At that point
Please, give them back.
'Til then,
I'll let you be."

GOODNIGHT CHILD

Memories layered brick by brick -
Foundation for the years beyond.
Each night, we whisper lovingly -
To reminisce and seal the bond.

"I do not want this day to end,"
the little one says with sleepy eyes.
And as my child drifts off to sleep,
I gaze, I warm, I empathize.

"I, too, don't want this day to end" -
A smile glows deep inside my heart.
Thankful that our storied future
Builds upon a loving start.

CAN YOU PLEASE HELP?

Thank you for reading this book!

We hope that you enjoyed reading and discussing
the poems. There are many books out there and
it is sometimes difficult to find one specific book.
This is where you can help!

You can help other readers find our books
by leaving a simple review and clicking on the stars.
A few minutes and a few words
would be greatly appreciated!

Your comments, good or bad, motivate us to keep
writing and providing high quality books for your enjoyment.
When you see new books from us in the future, you will
know that we wrote them because of your support.

Special thank you to previous readers and reviewers.

Thank you!
Edwin & Micah

POETRY PALS

ACKNOWLEDGEMENTS

All of these poems were inspired by personal life
experiences and frequent family silliness.

Thank you to those who provided feedback or a supportive
comment while this book series was evolving from idea to reality.
- Regan • Evelyn • Paddy
- Abhi • Stephanie • Chloé
- Cathy • Mike • Emmy • Lily
- Donovan • Cheryl • Elise • Miles • Wesley
- Terry • Marc • Meagan • Chip
- Sara • Heikki • Eevi • Enna
- Kara • Matt • Noah • Ashton • Zoe • Lana
- Michelle • Chloe
- Stephanie • Tom • Gabriel • Aria
- Paula • Kathy • Karen • Audrey
- Mae • Genevieve • Ayesha • Anji • Olivia • Lillian • Gwenn

A special thank you to Neda Sadreddin for perfectly complementing
our words with her simple and powerful imagery.

A special thank you also to Jean Meyer for her empathy,
her words, and her help to convey our simple messages
in the most profound way.

CPSIA information can be obtained
at www.ICGtesting.com
Printed in the USA
LVHW071309100921
697350LV00001BA/4

* 9 7 8 1 7 3 5 7 5 4 4 1 3 *